W9-CQH-792

Thankyou

We would like to thank our amazing followers for your continued support. Each moment you have shared with us has created lasting memories.
Thankyou for joining us on so many of our adventures and we hope you can join us for many more.

Jamie
x
Sherpa

Sherpa

In Search of Snow

Inspired by a real adventure

Written by Ellie Adkinson & Jamie Larder
Illustrated by Ellie Adkinson

'The sooner I fall asleep the sooner I get to find it' thought Sherpa as he lay there excited for snow, counting down the minutes as if it were the night before Christmas.

It had been a long journey to the Scottish mountains in the big red van he called home, and he knew endless fun and memories to come would last a lifetime.

With the comfort of his pillow, Sherpa's eyes slowly closed. That night he would dream of his winter adventures, exactly what snow dogs are made for.

"Hurry up!" howled a very happy boy, nudging Dad's head to wake him. "It's time!"

The morning sun had flooded the van with light and Sherpa didn't even think about his breakfast. As soon as the doors opened he leaped outside, eyes widened and wagging his tail so fast he almost took off!

'All of this for me?' he pondered as he took in the beautiful landscape and the promise of snow in the distance.

"Come on then Sherpy" said Dad.
"Let's go see what we can see".

Wandering along a path lined with fir trees that slowly
turned to ice was like a fairytale.
Paws started to slip in different directions and as he
skated forward Sherpa began to notice the ground
getting whiter and whiter.
The fresh crunchy snow beneath him as he
started to ascend the mountain was enough to send
him bounding with joy, running in
circles until he was met with an icy surprise
flying straight towards him and crashing
into his fluffy coat.
"Throw another snowball, I dare you!"
he teased as dad chased him.

Soon the path had disappeared into an endless frosty paradise, heavy snowfall with flakes that would land on Sherpa's nose as he sniffed the air to find his way through it.

With each paw print the snow would become deeper which meant they were getting closer and closer to the mountain peak.

This was turning into a blizzard!

Sherpa was eager to reach the top and began to pick up the pace.
"Slow down!" Dad yelled.
"There's too much snow!"
"There's no such thing as too much snow" woofed a determined Sherpa.
"This snow dog doesn't give up!"

As he reached the peak Sherpa stopped in his tracks.
Before him lay rich white valleys and a misty sky.
It was unlike anything he'd ever seen before and he
couldn't help but feel proud.
"Great things take time buddy" said his dad.
"This was completely worth battling our way through
that snowstorm."

The sun was starting to set and the snowfall began to ease. Bursts of orange covered everything in sight and two shadows were cast in front of them. As Dad pulled out his camera to capture the sunset, Sherpa posed in the funniest ways, skidding down slopes sending snow flying everywhere like a mini avalanche. "I think this entertainment deserves a reward" barked Sherpa.
"Think again" chuckled Dad.

By the time they had arrived back to their cosy camper the sky had been lit with stars and there was a chilly breeze in the air, perfect for wrapping up in wooly blankets.

Inside the van twinkly lights floated across the
ceiling and the smell of soup cooking on the stove
made this truly a home away from home.
Sherpa's tummy was instantly satisfied by a big bowl of
chicken and veggies perfectly topped with his
favourite sprats, washed down with spring
water and accompanied by a rub on the ear.

'The sooner I fall asleep, the sooner I get to come
back and find it again'
thought Sherpa as he lay there sleepy with a full
stomach and full imagination.
As Dad poured himself a cup of hot
chocolate and sat beside him, Sherpa's eyes
gradually moved up to look at him as if to say
'thankyou for everything'.
It was the perfect ending to the day and the most
amazing adventure, like so many had been
before.

CPSIA information can be obtained
at www.ICGtesting.com
Printed in the USA
BVRC101422201121
621926BV00008B/264

9 781739 805500